Nathan Levy's

STORIES WITH HOLES
VOLUME 16

Revised & Updated

By Nathan Levy

A collection of original thinking activities for improving inquiry!

A Nathan Levy Books, LLC Publication

Nathan Levy Books, LLC
18 Moorland Blvd
Monroe Twp, NJ 08831

ISBN 978-0-9840287-7-1

Printed in the United States of America

PREFACE – by Nathan Levy

This book is the result of several years accumulation of ideas leading to puzzling stories that lend themselves to what I call thinking games. The "games" have become the means for thousands of people to carry on a totally enjoyable process of engaging critical and imaginative thinking. Volume 1 of my Stories with Holes is a collection of stories that has been gathered from various sources. Nathan Levy's Stories with Holes Volumes 2-20 are original. Wherever I speak I share some of the stories with my training groups. Teachers, parents and children enjoy the stories immensely. I hope you will as well.

INTRODUCTION

The objectives of using Nathan Levy's Stories with Holes include the following:

- to provide for growth in imagination and intuitive functioning
- to give experiences that display the fun of working cooperatively, rather than competitively, on a common problem
- to increase cognitive skills of resolving discrepancies through successful experiences
- to provide enjoyable changes-of-pace for task-oriented learning environments

This is a structured activity. It is designed to ensure involvement on the part of each participant, and to promote feelings of group and individual success.

The games are designed to accommodate all levels. "Children" from ages 8-88 will benefit from using these stories.

The time a story takes will vary. Usually a story lasts from 3 to 30 minutes, but some stories can take days. Children, lower grades through high school, tend to regard these thinking games as play instead of work. It is one of the few activities I know of that "hooks" almost anyone into creative use of their intelligence, i.e. learning, almost in spite of themselves. Nathan Levy's Stories with Holes are for all groups over age seven, regardless of background or achievement level.

**Please note that I have revised the above introduction and the following methodology from the way they appeared in the original collection of Stories with Holes. The revisions are based on my current workshop experiences with children and adults.

N.L.

METHODOLOGY

The first time a group plays, it will be necessary to begin by announcing something like the following: "I am going to tell you a story with a hole in it – I mean that an important part of the story is missing. Listen carefully so you can find the missing part, for the story may not seem to make much sense to you at first…"

At this point, tell the story once, pause, and then tell it the same way again. Then say…

"You can ask questions that can be answered either with a "yes" or with a "no". I can only answer "yes", "no", "does not compute", or "is not relevant". If I answer, "does not compute", that means that the question you asked cannot receive a straight "yes" or "no" without throwing you off the track."

Allow for questions about the process, if there are any, but usually it is best simply to jump into the game by having the questioning start. The process becomes clear as the game progresses. Once a group has played the game, the full directions given above for playing the game are unnecessary.

From this point on, answer only in one of the four designated ways. The following is an example of a story taken from Stories with Holes, and how it might be played:

Story: "Mitch lives on the twentieth floor of an apartment building. Every time he leaves, he rides a self-service elevator from the twentieth floor to the street; but every time he returns, he rides the same self-service elevator only to the fifteenth floor, where he leaves the elevator and walks up the remaining five flights of stairs." Repeat, then ask who knows the answer already; if any do, ask them to observe and not give away the answer.

Question: Does the elevator go all the way up?
Answer: Yes.
Q: Does he want the exercise?
A: No.
Q: Does it have something to do with the elevator not working right?
A: No.
Q: Does he have a girlfriend on the 15th floor who he stops to see?
A: No.
Q: Does he have something different about him?
A: Yes.
Q: Is he a robber?
A: No.
Q: Is he a real person?
A: Yes.
Q: A tall person?
A: No.
Q: Is his size important?
A: Yes.
Q: I know! He's too short to reach the button!
A: Right!

At this point, make certain that all the participants understand the answer and why it is the correct answer. In the example given above, the group found the answer quite soon. Instead of starting a new game -- particularly if this is the first time playing – spend some time processing the game with questions like:

* What did you have to do in order to play this game? (Listen, hear each answer, think, imagine, follow a line of reasoning, eliminate possibilities, etc.)

* Ask the person who finally solved the riddle, "Joanne, did you have help from others in finding the answer?" It nearly always comes out that the person relied on previous questions and answers. Use this to point out the interdependence of players, and reduce competition within the group to be the "winner".

* When do you see yourself having to use the kind of thinking you use in this game?

Usually a group of youngsters will be eager to try a second game right away.

Some important points to remember:

1. Immediately following the telling of each story and before the questioning begins, ask if anyone in the group has heard it before and knows the answer. Tell these people to observe and refrain from questioning.

2. Use the "does not compute" response whenever a single word or phrase in a question makes it impossible to answer with a "yes" or "no" answer. Examples from the story above:

- "Why does he live on the twentieth floor?" "Why" questions, as well as "where, who, when or which", cannot be answered "yes" or "no".

- "Does the elevator operator make him get off at the fifteenth floor?" No mention was made of an operator.

3. If a game goes past 10 or 12 minutes and some people begin to lose interest, close the game for the present. There is absolutely nothing harmful in leaving the puzzle unsolved. The group can return to it another time, when interest and energy are high. Some students may protest, but do not give the answer. The experience of non-closure provides some valuable learning in itself; but more importantly, once a group has expended considerable energy on the game, the victory should be an earned one. Although there may be some unusual circumstances under which you would give the group the answer, I have found it best not to do so (even if some are begging). The point here is not to "take the answer away by giving it." You can always return to it later. What is important is that the students earn the feeling of "we-did-it!"

4. Share the leader role. Once kids have learned how the game works, have a volunteer lead the game. He or she must choose from the stories he or she already

knows. As soon as you are convinced the student is familiar with the story, the answer, and the process (which you should previously have modeled) have the leader read the story to the class, and begin taking questions. Most important here is what you model. A child-led game is an excellent small-group activity to have going on while you are occupied elsewhere in the classroom.

5. You may periodically want to encourage categorical thinking. When a player asks a question beginning, "Would it help us to know…" or "Does it have anything to do with…" pause in the game and show how the type of question is uniquely helpful in narrowing down the range of questions, distilling and focusing the group's attention, or cutting away large slices of the topic that are irrelevant. Thus, the question "Is David's occupation important?" tends to be more useful than "Is he a plumber? A teacher?" etc.

6. Be sure that a question is exactly true, or exactly false, before responding. One word can make the difference.

OTHER TITLES DISTRIBUTED BY NATHAN LEVY BOOKS LLC

Bright Kids Who Can't Learn
Breakfast for the Brain
If Picasso Had a Christmas Tree
If Picasso Went to the Zoo
The Nearly Empty Coloring Book
The Inspirational Sketchbook
The Interactive Sketchbook
65 Short Mysteries You Solve with Math
65 Short Mysteries You Solve with Science
65 More Short Mysteries You Solve with Science
101 Things Everyone Should Know about Math
101 Things Everyone Should Know about Science
See Jane Win
How Jane Won
So You Want to be a Screenwriter
How Long Can a Fly Fly?
Why Can't Potatoes Walk?
Integrating Science with Mathematics & Literacy
Active Lessons for Active Brains
The Developing Brain – From Birth to Age Eight

1. Crossing the River

A man wanted to row across a river with his pet weasel, a rooster, and some corn. The only available boat was so small that he could only carry one item with him at the time. To complicate the problem, the weasel, if left alone, would eat the rooster, and the rooster would eat the corn. How did he cross the river with his possessions intact?

Answer:

The man took the rooster to the other side first, then rowed back to get the weasel. He rowed the weasel across, left it on the other side, but brought the rooster back and left it on the shore. He then brought the corn across, rowed back and brought the rooster across again.

2. The All - Night Market

Ingrid, who is always quick to panic, went food shopping in an all-night market and parked her car in a distant part of the parking lot. As she completed her shopping, all the electricity in the market went off. The emergency parking lights were not on. She did not have her flashlight. She calmly and quickly located her car.

Answer:

It was early afternoon when she finished shopping. She had to find it in the daylight.

3. Uncle's Dream

When Libby was asked how her uncle had died, she explained: "My uncle was reading a novel. It was so boring that he fell asleep. While he was sleeping he had a horrible dream about being attacked by a prehistoric dinosaur. Uncle Joe got so frightened, he had a heart attack and died immediately." Obviously, Libby is not telling the truth.

Answer:

If Uncle Joe died immediately, how could Libby know about his dream?

4. The Cylindrical Barrel

Pierre wanted to fill a cylindrical barrel of wine half full. He had no instruments to measure the amount of wine he was using, but he was able to fill the barrel exactly half full. How?

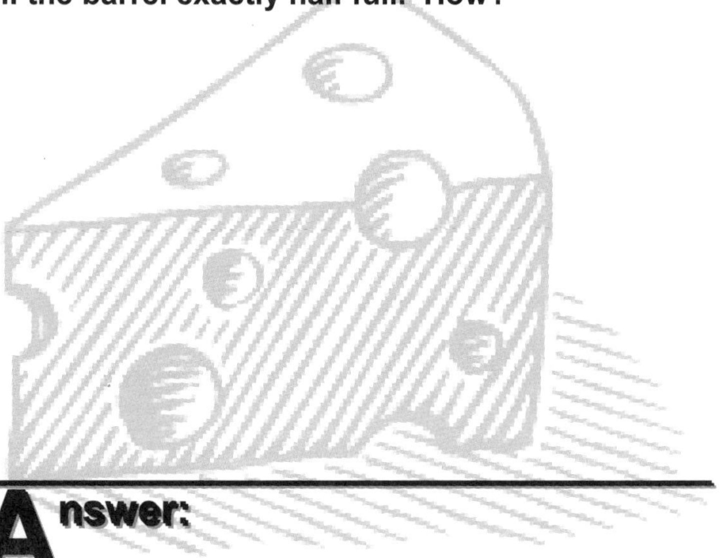

Answer:

He filled the wine barrel more than half full. Then he tilted the barrel and poured out the wine until the wine covered the top and the bottom of the barrel. The barrel was then exactly half full.

5. Rick and Dawn

"You sure are lucky I was here to pull you out of the water, Rick. The boat ladder seemed to be out of your reach. You would have drowned."

"Never, Dawn. A wave was coming that would have helped me reach the ladder to pull myself to safety."

"Think again, Rick."

"Thanks, Dawn, you saved my life."

Answer:

Rick realized that the wave would have raised the boat and the ladder as it raised him; thus, he still would not be able to reach the ladder.

6. The Dogs

The dogs remained frozen, even though their owners, Jane and Bob, were so hot they were swimming in the lake.

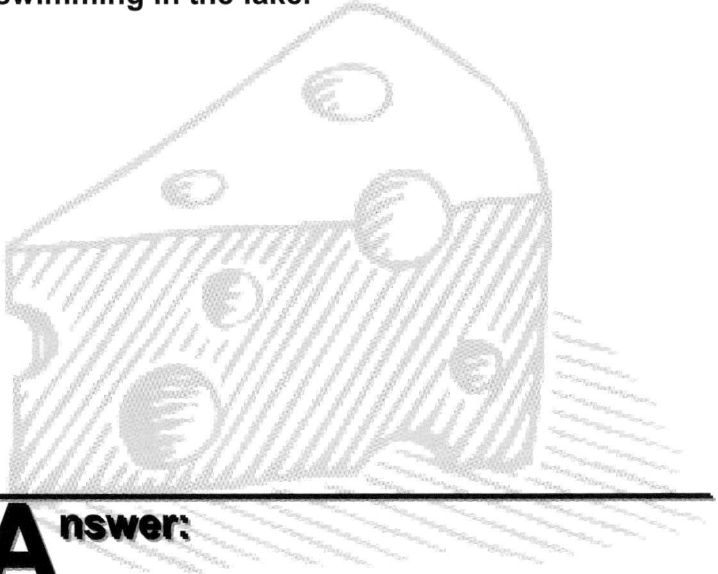

Answer:

The “dogs” were hot dogs (frankfurters) which had been frozen prior to being packed in the cooler for Jane and Bob’s picnic.

7. Egyptian Confusion

Many people who hear about the Egyptian people believe negative things. While they are wrong, it is understandable given the reports that come out in the news media about Egypt. Why?

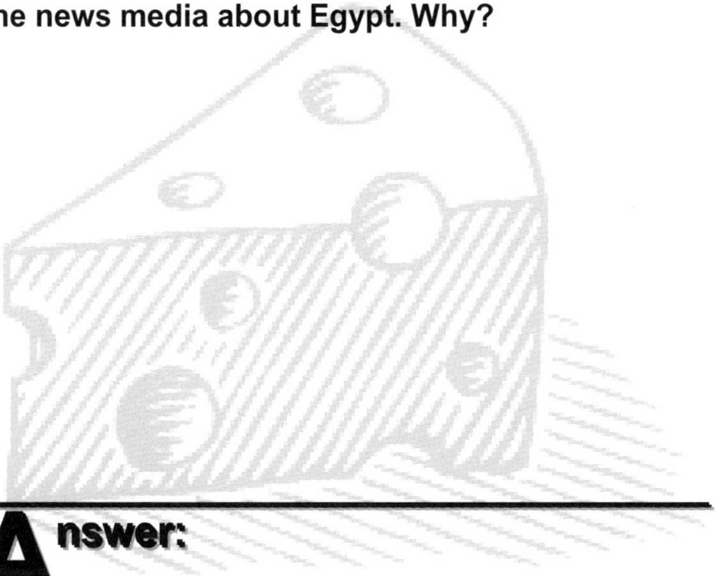

Answer:

Many news reports announce that Egyptians do many things and spend much time in the Nile, heard as "denial". This leaves ignorant listeners with the wrong impression of what reports are saying.

8. The Bet

Marci bet Joanne she could put the water from her goldfish bowl and the water from her guppy bowl into one large tank (with no separations) and then put the water from the large tank back into the original bowls without mixing the water. To Joanne's astonishment, Marci succeeded.

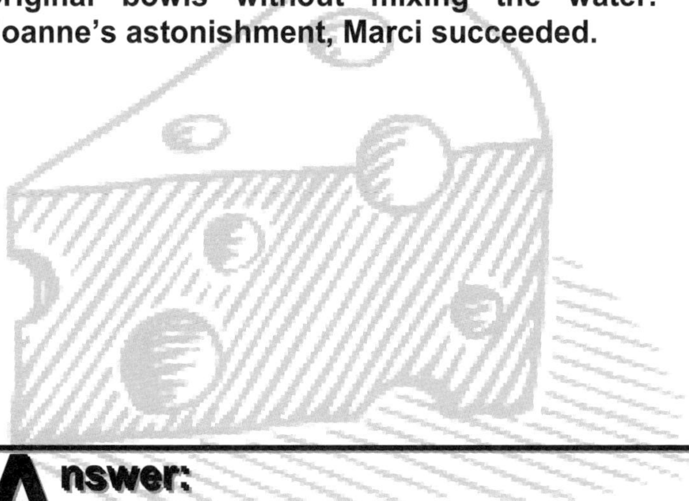

Answer:

Marci froze the water in each bowl before putting it into the large tank. She then picked up the ice chunks from each bowl and put them back into the original bowls.

9. Breaking of Day

Every dawn begins with me,
At dusk I'll be the first you see,
And daybreak couldn't come without
What midday centers all about.
Daisies grow from me, I'm told
And when I come, I end all cold,
But in the sun I won't be found,
Yet still, each day I'll be around.

Answer:

The letter D.

10. The Pet Poodle

My friend woke up one morning and found his pet lying motionless on the floor. When he couldn't arouse him, he rushed him to the veterinarian. The vet could find no sign of life and let his cat examine the poodle as well. After climbing all over the poodle, the cat gave a sad meow and retreated. Then the vet's Labrador Retriever also climbed over the poodle with the same negative results. When the vet gave him the sad news, my friend asked for the bill. $450! He exclaimed...why so much? My fee is only $150, the vet replied, but...

Answer:

There was the CAT scan and the lab report! (the cat and the Labrador Retriever).

11. The Weights

A scientist had 9 weights that looked alike, but one weight weighed more than the others. Using a balance to determine which weight was the odd one, how did the scientist find the heavier weight in two weighings?

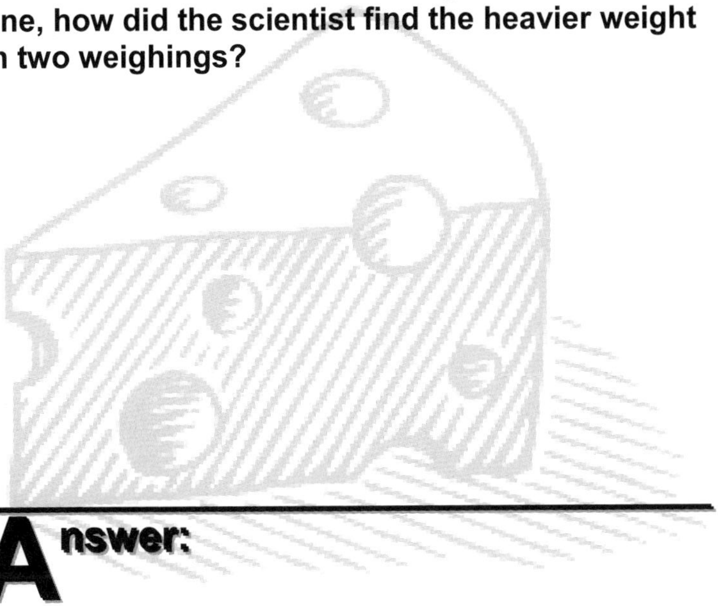

Answer:

He weighs 3 on each side first. If they balance, then he picks 2 more and weighs them. If they balance he has located the heavier weight because it has not yet been weighed. If they do not balance, by looking at the scale, he can tell which is heavier. He then takes the 3 from the heavier side and repeats the process by weighing 2 weights to determine which is the heavier. If they balance, then the remaining weight must be heavier.

12. The Housing Development

"The name of our housing development is meant to guarantee safety and security," explained the real estate agent, Jim Watson.
"The name of this development certainly makes me feel secure – especially with you as the agent."

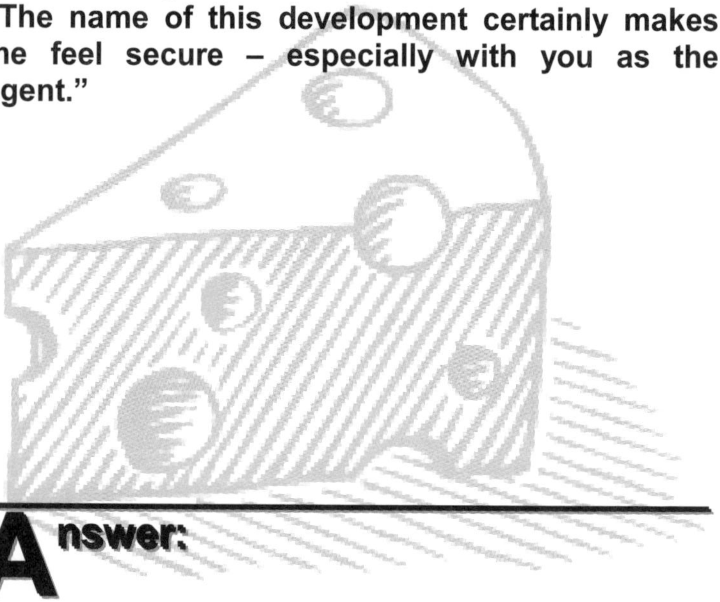

Answer:

Sherlock Homes (Holmes) was the name of the housing development.

13. The Long Drive

Sam, the truck driver drove a huge oil rig from Massachusetts to California. Not once did Sam use a men's room during the entire 3,000 mile trip.

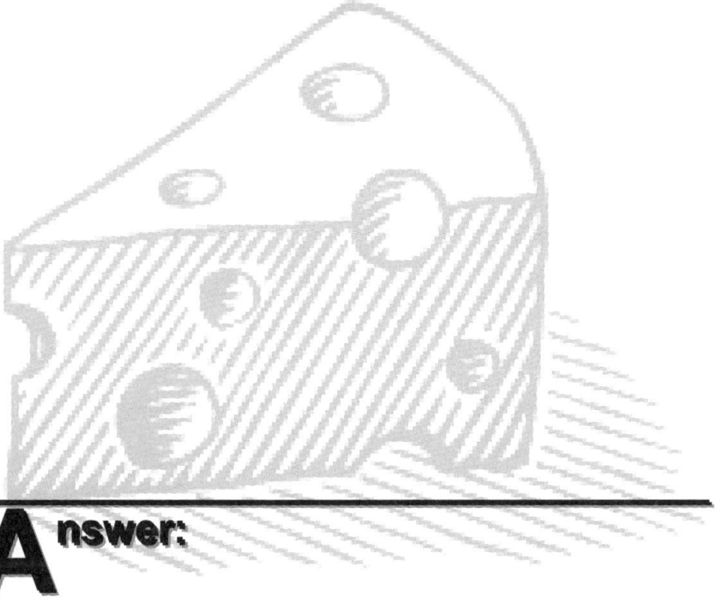

Answer:

Sam is a woman.

.

14. The Scientist

James Bond was assigned the task of stopping the mad inventor. The scientist had threatened "literally to destroy London with huge vials of liquid that would dissolve anything." James Bond refused the assignment because he knew there was no threat.

Answer:

If the liquid could dissolve anything, there could be nothing that could hold the liquid.

15. The Snake

The snake's presence saved the Fischbeins from a disastrous flood.

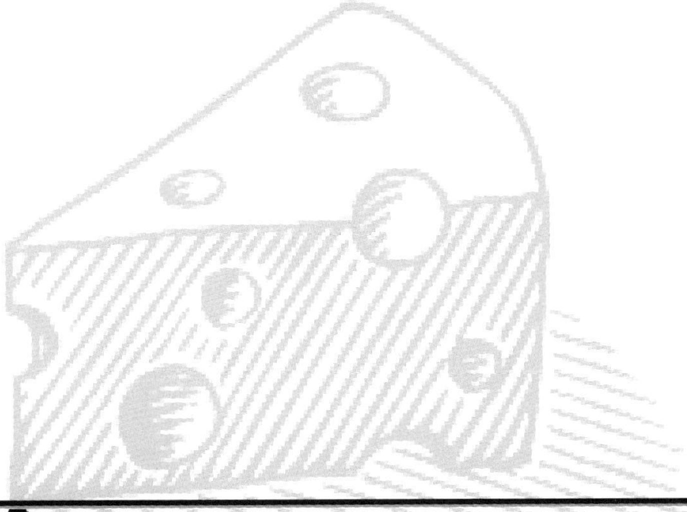

Answer:

The "snake" was used by the plumber to clear out the clogged pipe which was about to overflow into the house.

16. The Signpost

"Don't worry," said the man giving directions. "There's a signpost a mile down the road which will point you in the right direction for the town of Monmouth Junction." As the truck driver approached the sign after he left town, he had found that the sign had been knocked over. Where he had been, told him how to get where he was going.

Answer:

He got out of the truck and pointed the signpost in the direction of the town he recently left. By matching the sign for that town, he could then figure out how to get to Monmouth Junction.

17. Nicholas the Famous Fisherman

Nicholas, the famous fisherman, had won a trip to a unique fishing location. As he carried his fishing rod – collapsed into 5 foot sections – towards the plane, he was told of an airline rule prohibiting items on the plane or in storage that are more than 4 feet long. A few hours later, Nicholas was happily fishing with his favorite rod which he had taken with him on the plane.

Answer:

Nicholas had placed the 5-foot rod segments diagonally in a 3' by 4' crate which could be transported.

18. The Hospital

The hospital had a firm rule that all televisions must be turned off by 10 p.m. each and every evening. On Saturday evening, March 27, 2025, 17 patients were sitting and watching television at 11.15 p.m.

Answer:

The patients broke the rule.

19. Father

The father was measured – again. Not one of the "measurers" ever cares about his height, weight, or girth.

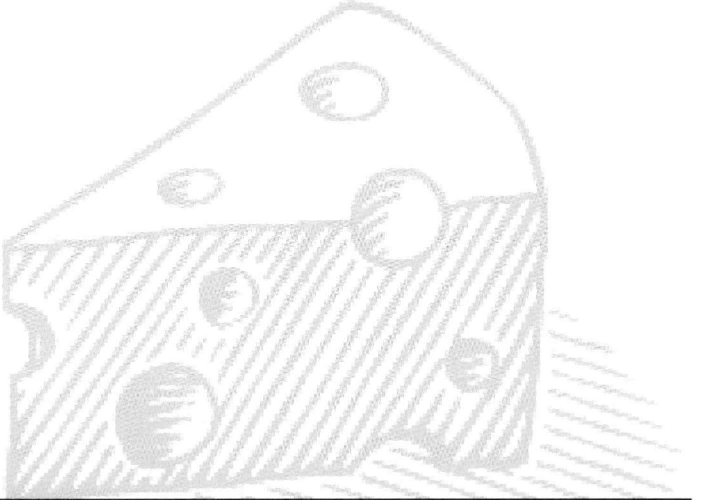

Answer:

He is "Father Time".

20. The Messy Restaurant

Mr. & Mrs. Neach were visiting a small town in Alaska for the very first time. They were very hungry. The town had only two restaurants. The Neaches found the first restaurant to be very messy. It seemed as if it did not have enough help to keep it clean. The second restaurant was spotlessly clean. The Neaches ate their lunch at the first restaurant.

Answer:

The first restaurant was so much messier because the local people ate there so often that the restaurant workers did not have time to keep it clean during lunch. Obviously, the second restaurant's owners never had customers who like the food, so they could keep their restaurant spotlessly clean.

ABOUT THE AUTHOR

Nathan Levy

Nathan Levy is the author of more than 40 books which have sold almost 250,000 copies to teachers and parents in the United States, Europe, Asia, South America, Australia and Africa. His unique Stories with Holes series continues to be proclaimed the most popular activity used in gifted, special education and regular classrooms by hundreds of educators. An extremely popular, dynamic speaker on thinking, writing and differentiation, Nathan is in high demand as a workshop leader in school and business settings. He has worked as a school principal, district supervisor, gifted coordinator, is a company president, parent of four daughters and management trainer. Nathan's ability to transfer knowledge and strategies to audiences through humorous, thought provoking stories assures that participants leave with a plethora of new ways to approach their future endeavors.

Nathan Levy Books, LLC is pleased to be the publisher of this book. Teachers, students and other readers are invited to contribute their own "Stories with Holes" for possible inclusion in future volumes. Suggested stories will not be returned to you and will be acknowledged only if selected. Please send your suggestions to:

Nathan Levy Books, LLC
(732) 605 -1643
NLevy103@comcast.net